This Book Belongs To:

_____

GOODBYE!

The last day of school will be

_____

My Teacher this school year was

My Favorite Subject

My favorite book this year was

Three things
I learned this year

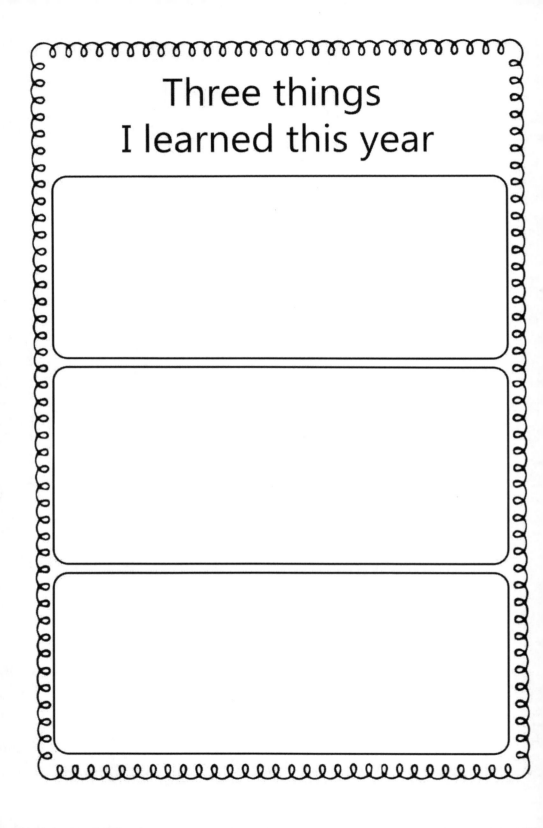

One goal I achieved was

One thing I will always remember

The Funniest Moment

On field trip day we went to

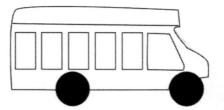

My favorite outdoor game

My favorite school lunch

My favorite song

Next year I will be in ___ grade.

I hope my teacher is

I want to learn more about

Three words that best describe you...

I will never forget...

Autograph:

Three words that best describe you...

I will never forget...

Autograph:

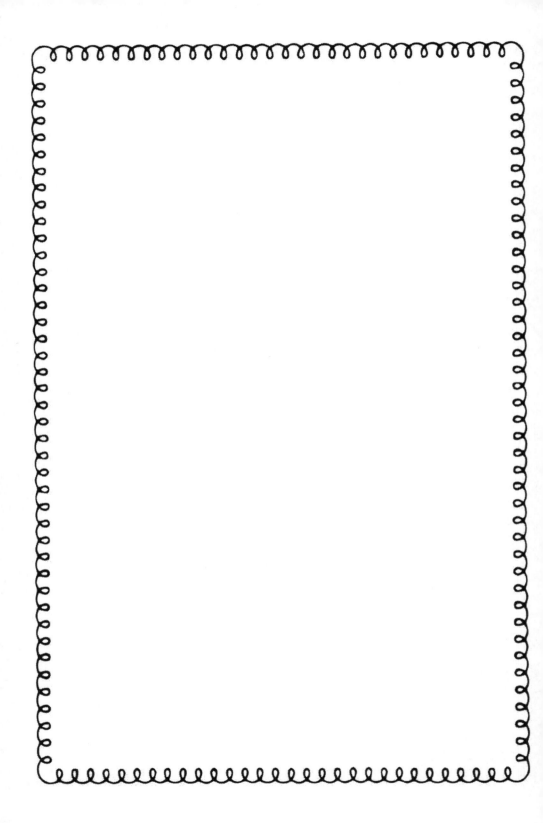

Three words that best describe you...

I will never forget...

Autograph:

Three words that best describe you...

I will never forget...

Autograph:

Three words that best describe you...

I will never forget...

Autograph:

Three words that best describe you...

I will never forget...

Autograph:

Three words that best describe you...

I will never forget...

Autograph:

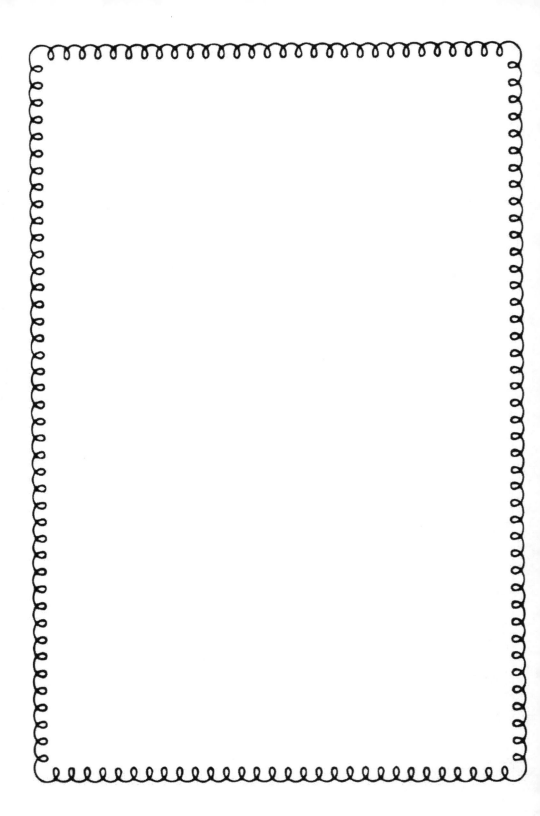

Three words that best describe you...

I will never forget...

Autograph:

Three words that best describe you...

I will never forget...

Autograph:

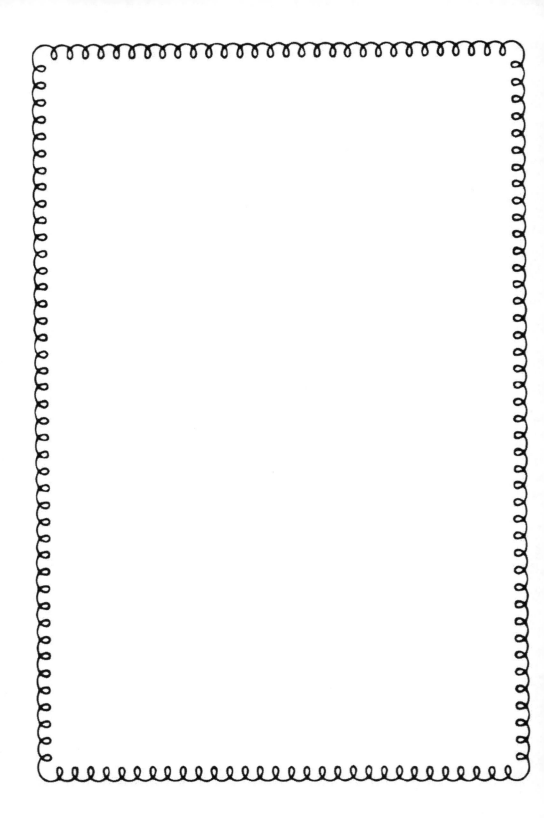

Three words that best describe you...

I will never forget...

Autograph:

Three words that best describe you...

I will never forget...

Autograph:

Three words that best describe you...

I will never forget...

Autograph:

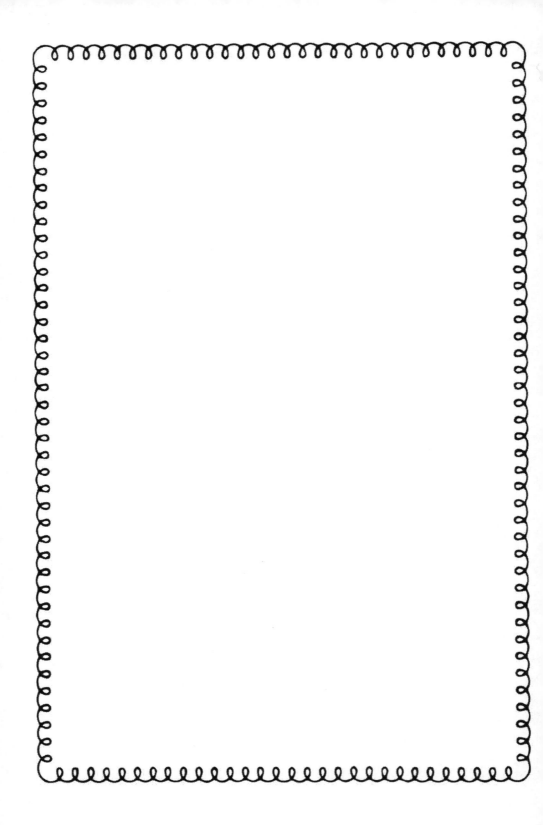

Three words that best describe you...

I will never forget...

Autograph:

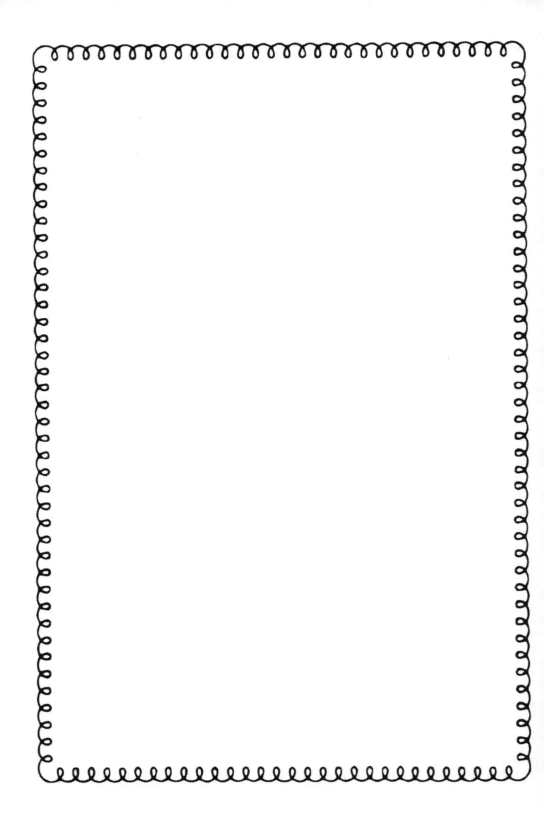

Three words that best describe you...

I will never forget...

Autograph:

Three words that best describe you...

I will never forget...

Autograph:

Three words that best describe you...

I will never forget...

Autograph:

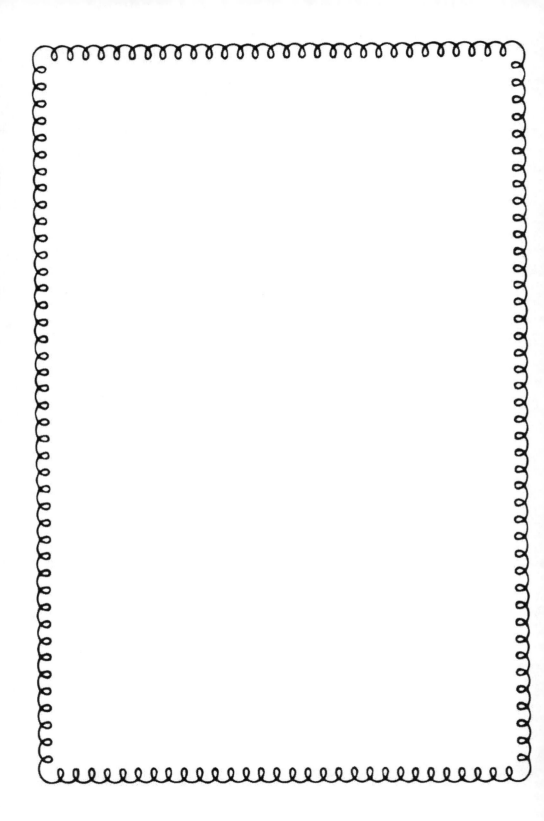

Three words that best describe you...

I will never forget...

Autograph:

Three words that best describe you...

I will never forget...

Autograph:

Three words that best describe you...

I will never forget...

Autograph:

Three words that best describe you...

I will never forget...

Autograph:

Three words that best describe you...

I will never forget...

Autograph:

Three words that best describe you...

I will never forget...

Autograph:

Three words that best describe you...

I will never forget...

Autograph:

Three words that best describe you...

I will never forget...

Autograph:

Three words that best describe you...

I will never forget...

Autograph:

Three words that best describe you...

I will never forget...

Autograph:

Three words that best describe you...

I will never forget...

Autograph:

Three words that best describe you...

I will never forget...

Autograph:

Three words that best describe you...

I will never forget...

Autograph:

Three words that best describe you...

I will never forget...

Autograph:

Three words that best describe you...

I will never forget...

Autograph:

Three words that best describe you...

I will never forget...

Autograph:

Three words that best describe you...

I will never forget...

Autograph:

Three words that best describe you...

I will never forget...

Autograph:

Three words that best describe you...

I will never forget...

Autograph:

Three words that best describe you...

I will never forget...

Autograph:

Three words that best describe you...

I will never forget...

Autograph:

Three words that best describe you...

I will never forget...

Autograph:

Three words that best describe you...

I will never forget...

Autograph:

Three words that best describe you...

I will never forget...

Autograph:

Three words that best describe you...

I will never forget...

Autograph:

Three words that best describe you...

I will never forget...

Autograph:

OTHER AVAILABLE BOOKS

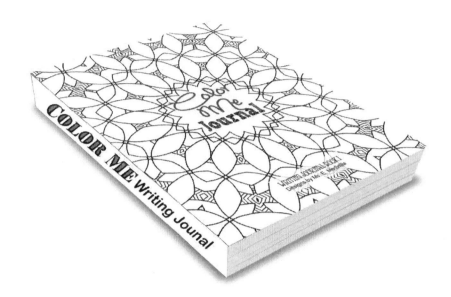

Visit us at MAACBooks.com to see what
other books we have ready for you to color.

Join our fan page and share
your colored pages with us!

https://www.facebook.com/maacbooks/